Primo Piano. Easy Piano Music for Adults

55 Timeless Piano Songs for Adult Beginners with Downloadable Audio

Aria Altmann

Edited by Dragutin Jovičić

Primo Piano. Easy Piano Music for Adults. 55 Timeless Piano Songs for Adult Beginners with Downloadable Audio by Aria Altmann

Copyright © 2021 by **Sontig Press**

2. edition 2021
ISBN: 978-3-9822692-1-4
Sontig Press

Contents

PREFACE

1. Ode to Joy (Anthem of Europe) 1

2. Brother John (Frère Jacques) 2

3. Happy Birthday 3

4. This Land Is Your Land 4

5. I Saw Three Ships 5

6. Auld Lang Syne 6

7. Amazing Grace 7

8. Aura Lee 8

9. What Shall We Do with the Drunken Sailor 9

10. She'll Be Coming 'Round the Mountain 10

11. Scotland The Brave 11

12. Kum Ba Yah 12

13. Die Gedanken sind frei... 13

14. America The Beautiful 14

15. Tumbalalaika 15

16. My Bonnie Lies Over the Ocean 17

17. Oh, My Darling, Clementine 19

18. Banks of the Ohio 20

19. When the Saints Go Marching In 21

20. Wer ein Liebchen hat gefunden 22

21. Theme from the New World Symphony 23

22. For He's a Jolly Good Fellow 25

23. Spring 26

24. 'O sole mio 27

25. The Star-Spangled Banner 29

26. Sleeping Beauty Waltz 31

27. Wild Rover 32

28. Can Can 33

29. Oh, Susanna! 35

30. La donna è mobile (Rigoletto) 36

31. Greensleeves 37

32. Habanera (Carmen) 39

33. Minuet in G major 41

34. God Save The Queen 42

35. The Oak and the Ash 43

36. Toreador Song (Carmen) 45

37. Bella Ciao 46

38. Tarantella Napoletana 47

39. Minuet in D Minor 49

40. Eine kleine Nachtmusik 50

41. Allegro in F major, K.1c 51

42. Swan Lake 52

43. Wedding March 53

44. Scarborough Fair 55

45. The Blue Danube 57

46. Für Elise 59

47. Caprice No. 24 60

48. The Entertainer 61

49. The Swan (Le Cygne) 63

50. March (The Nutcracker) 65

51. Der Hölle Rache (The Magic Flute) 68

52. Symphony No. 40 (Great G minor symphony) 71

53. Turkish March (Turkish Rondo) 73

54. Hungarian Dance No. 5 75

55. Adagio cantabile (Sonata Pathétique) 77

FREE AUDIO FILES

OTHER BOOKS

Preface

Designed especially for beginning pianists, *Primo Piano. Easy Piano Music for Adults* will bring the joy of music to the adult piano student: be it younger or beginning adults as well as returning adult students.

These carefully selected songs and classical pieces have been arranged and simplified to develop the hands and ears of the performer, allowing them to experience beautiful music that otherwise might have been too challenging.

The book includes a beautiful and varied mix of well-known and some less known folk songs and pieces of classical music – both from the English-speaking countries as well as internationally.

The songs in the book are organized in order of increasing expertise: the easier pieces appear at the beginning of the book with the level of difficulty gradually rising to more challenging pieces at the end.

For some songs at challenging places, fingerings have been provided as a suggestion, but should not be considered absolute, since each pair of hands playing these arrangements is unique.

Ode to Joy
(Anthem of Europe)

Music: Ludwig van Beethoven

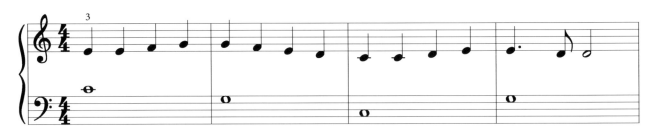

Brother John
(Frère Jacques)

French Nursery Rhyme

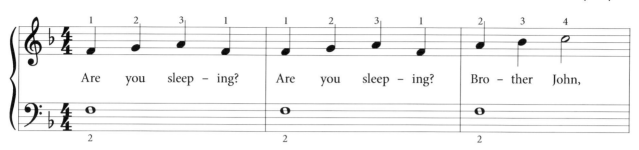

Are you sleep – ing? Are you sleep – ing? Bro – ther John,

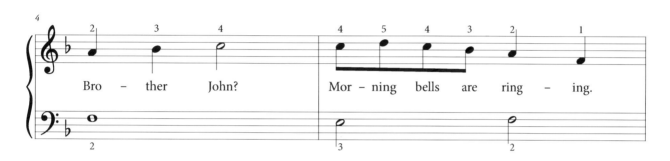

Bro – ther John? Mor – ning bells are ring – ing.

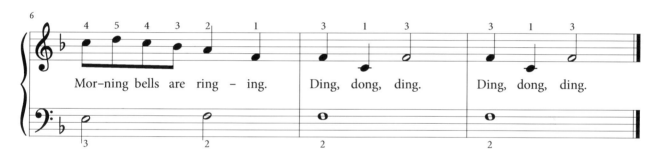

Mor – ning bells are ring – ing. Ding, dong, ding. Ding, dong, ding.

Happy Birthday

Folk Song

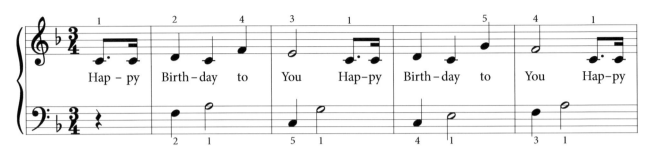

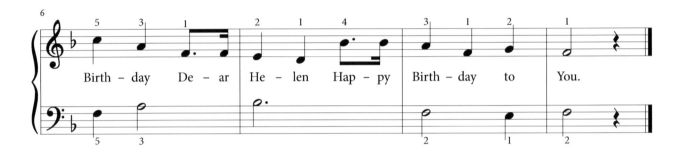

This Land Is Your Land

Music: American Folk Song
Lyrics: Woody Guthrie

I Saw Three Ships

English Folk Song

Auld Lang Syne

Music: Scottish folk song
Lyrics: Robert Burns

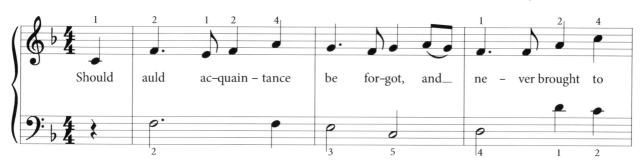

Should auld ac-quain-tance be for-got, and ne - ver brought to

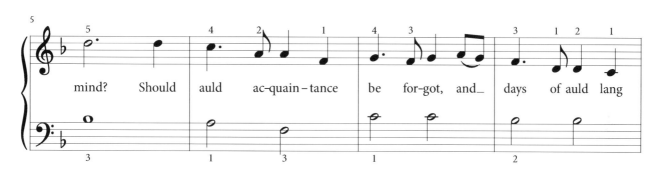

mind? Should auld ac-quain-tance be for-got, and days of auld lang

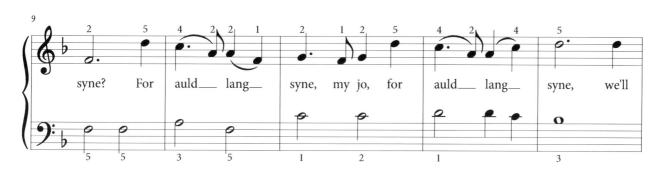

syne? For auld lang syne, my jo, for auld lang syne, we'll

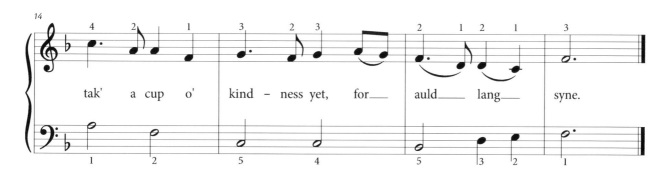

tak' a cup o' kind - ness yet, for auld lang syne.

Amazing Grace

Music: Traditional
Lyrics: John Newton

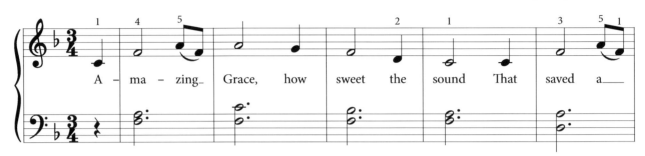

A - ma - zing_ Grace, how sweet the sound That saved a__

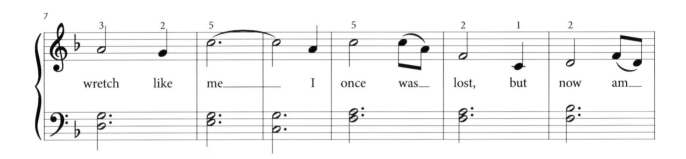

wretch like me____ I once was__ lost, but now am__

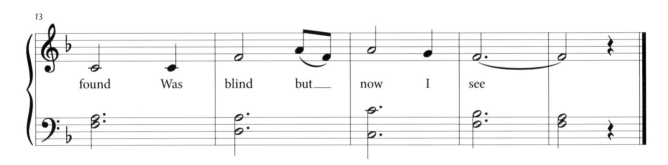

found Was blind but__ now I see

Aura Lee

Music: George R. Poulton
Lyrics: W. W. Fosdick

When the black – bird in the Spring, On the wil – low tree,

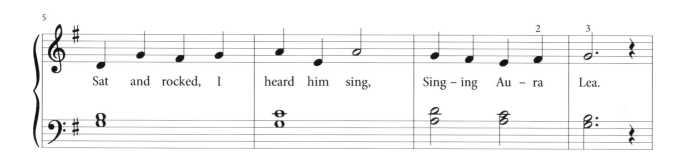

Sat and rocked, I heard him sing, Sing – ing Au – ra Lea.

Au – ra Lea, Au – ra Lea, Maid with gold – en hair;

Sun – shine came a – long with thee, And swal – lows in the air.

What Shall We Do with the Drunken Sailor

Folk Song

She'll Be Coming 'Round the Mountain

American Folksong

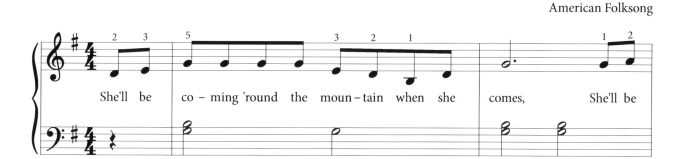

Scotland The Brave

Scottish Patriotic Song

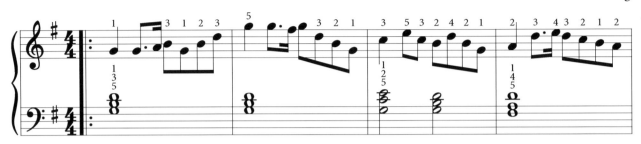

Kum Ba Yah

African American Spiritual

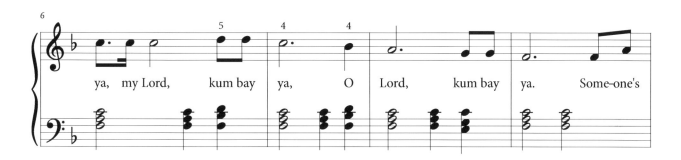

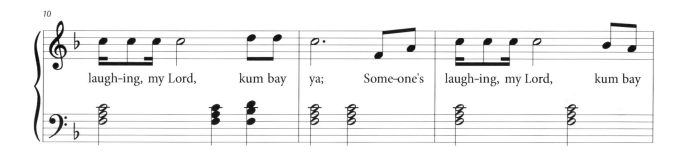

Die Gedanken sind frei

German Folk Song

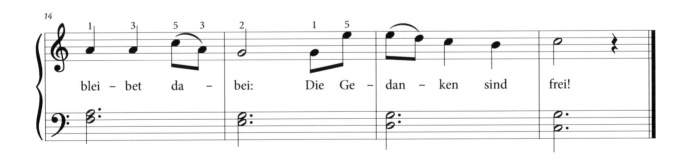

America The Beautiful

Music: Samuel A. Ward
Lyrics: Katharine Lee Bates

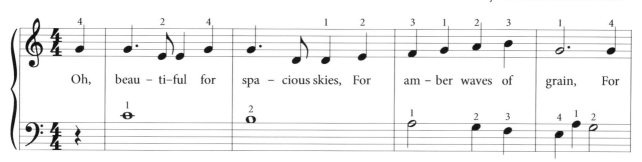

Oh, beau - ti-ful for spa - cious skies, For am - ber waves of grain, For

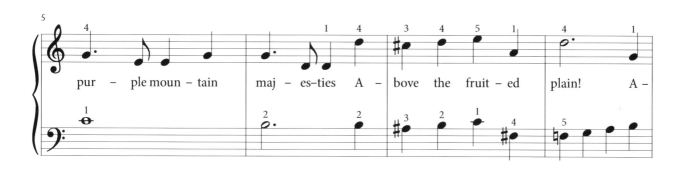

pur – ple moun - tain maj - es-ties A - bove the fruit - ed plain! A-

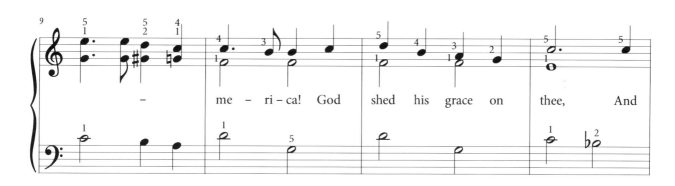

– me - ri - ca! God shed his grace on thee, And

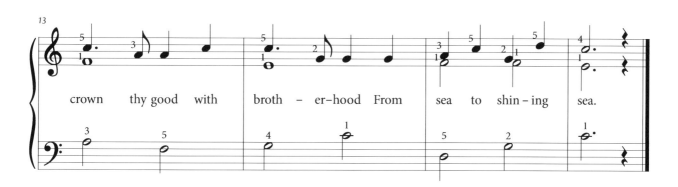

crown thy good with broth - er-hood From sea to shin - ing sea.

Tumbalalaika

Russian Jewish Folk Song

My Bonnie Lies over the Ocean

Scottish Folk Song

Oh My Darling, Clementine

Music: American Folksong
Lyrics: Percy Montrose

Oh my dar – ling, oh my dar – ling, Oh my dar – ling, Cle-men-

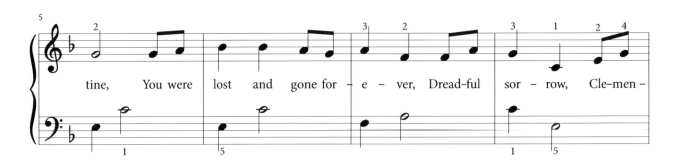

tine, You were lost and gone for – e – ver, Dread-ful sor – row, Cle-men-

tine. In a ca – vern, in a ca – nyon, Ex-ca-va – ting for a mine, Dwelt a

mi – ner for – ty – ni – ner, And his daugh – ter, Cle-men – tine.

Banks of the Ohio

American Folk Song

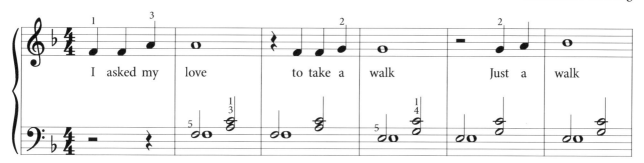

I asked my love to take a walk Just a walk

a lit – tle way And as we walk, oh, may we talk

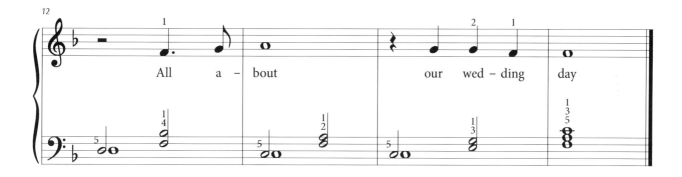

All a – bout our wed – ding day

When the Saints Go Marching In

Gospel song

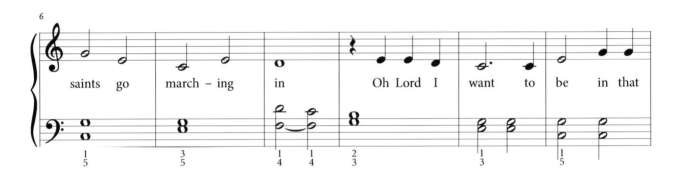

Wer ein Liebchen hat gefunden

(The Abduction from the Seraglio)

Wolfgang Amadeus Mozart

Theme from the New World Symphony

Antonín Dvořák

For He's a Jolly Good Fellow

Folk Song

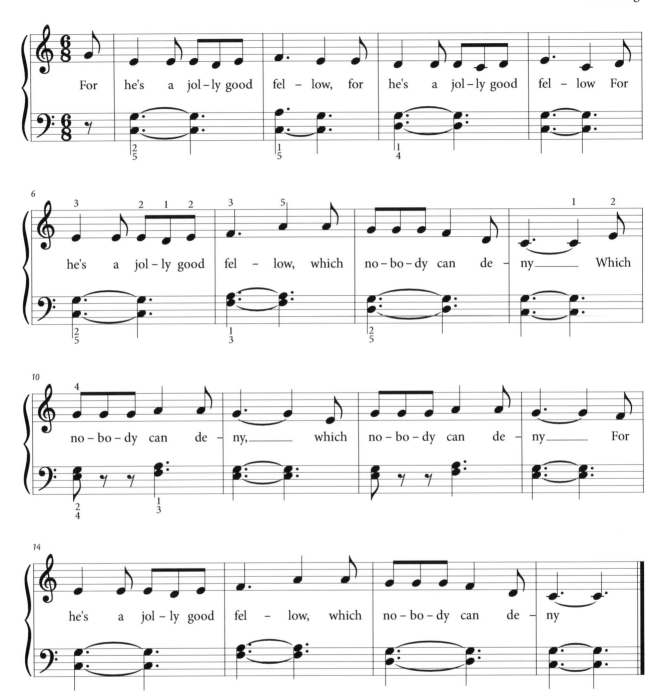

Spring

Antonio Vivaldi

'O sole mio

Music: Eduardo Di Capua, Alfredo Mazzucchi
Lyrics: Giovanni Capurro

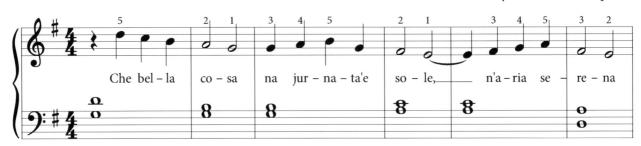

Che bel – la   co – sa   na   jur – na – ta'e   so – le,___   n'a – ria   se – re – na

dop – po   na   tem – pes – ta;___   Pe'   ll'a – ria   fre – sca   pa – re   gia'   na

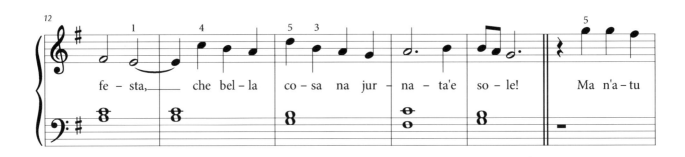

fe – sta,___   che bel – la   co – sa na jur – na – ta'e   so – le!   Ma   n'a – tu

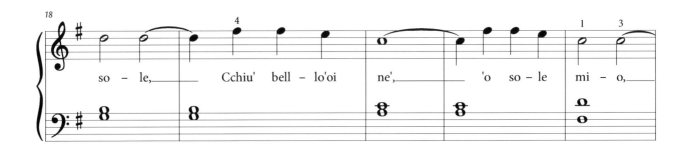

so – le,___   Cchiu'   bell – lo'oi   ne',   'o   so – le   mi – o,___

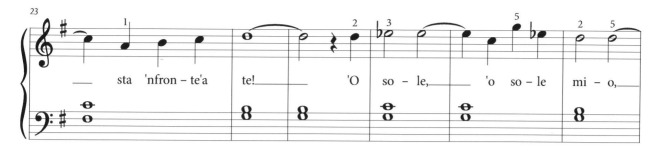

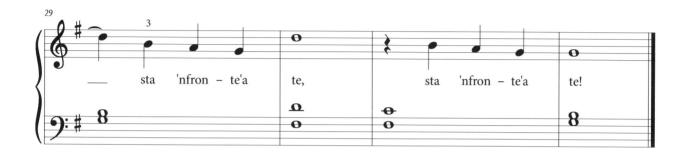

The Star-Spangled Banner
(National Anthem of the United States)

Music: John Stafford Smith
Lyrics: Francis Scott Key

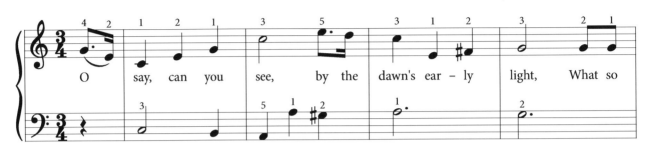

O say, can you see, by the dawn's ear - ly light, What so

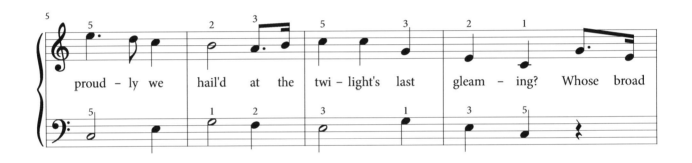

proud - ly we hail'd at the twi - light's last gleam - ing? Whose broad

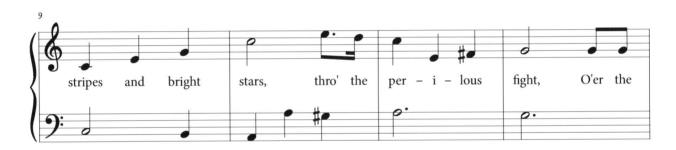

stripes and bright stars, thro' the per - i - lous fight, O'er the

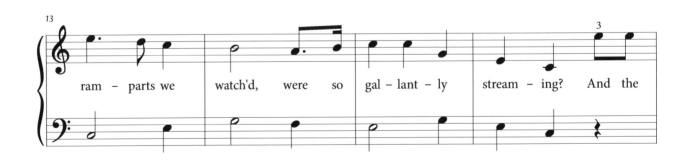

ram - parts we watch'd, were so gal - lant - ly stream - ing? And the

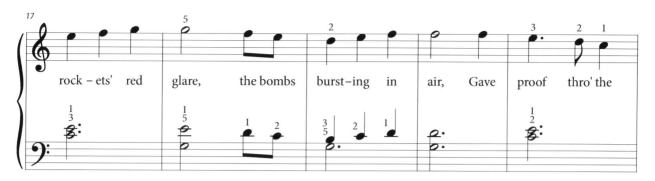

rock – ets' red glare, the bombs burst–ing in air, Gave proof thro' the

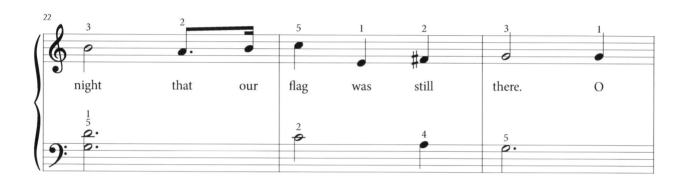

night that our flag was still there. O

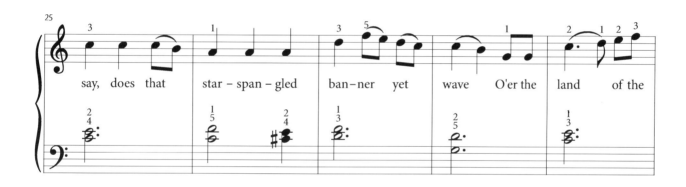

say, does that star – span – gled ban–ner yet wave O'er the land of the

free and the home of the brave?

Sleeping Beauty Waltz

Pyotr Ilyich Tchaikovsky

Wild Rover

Irish Folk Song

Can Can

Jacques Offenbach

Oh, Susanna!

Music & Lyrics: Stepen Foster

La donna è mobile
(Rigoletto)

Giuseppe Verdi

Greensleeves

English Folk Song

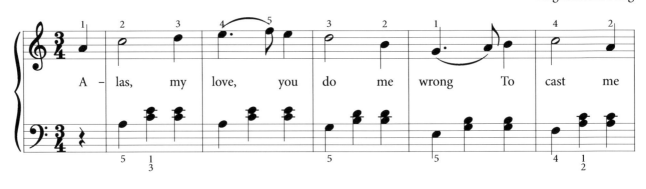

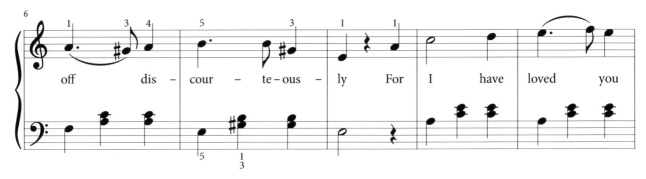

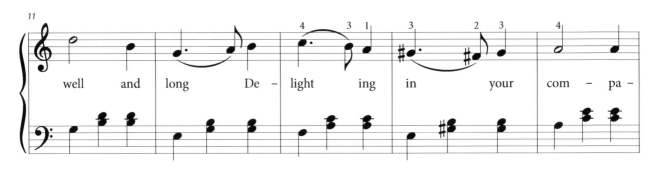

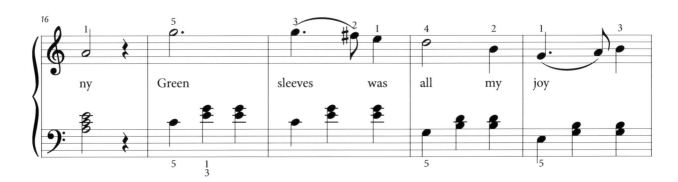

Green sleeves was my de – light Green
sleeves was my heart of gold And who but my
la dy green sleeves

Habanera
(Carmen)

Georges Bizet

Minuet in G major

Christian Petzold

God Save The Queen

(National Anthem of the United Kingdom
and one of two national anthems of New Zealand)

Traditional (also attributed to John Bull)

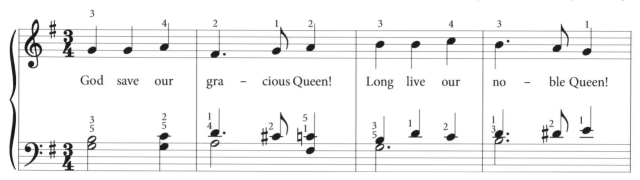

God save our gra – cious Queen! Long live our no – ble Queen!

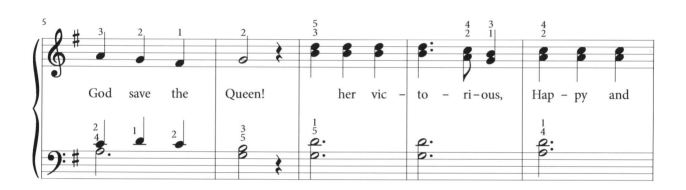

God save the Queen! her vic – to – ri–ous, Hap – py and

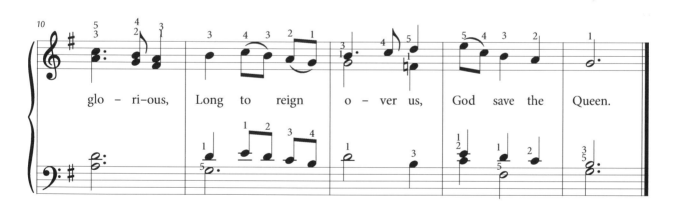

glo – ri–ous, Long to reign o – ver us, God save the Queen.

The Oak and the Ash

English Folk Song

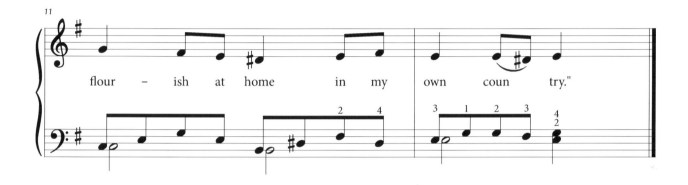

Toreador Song
(Carmen)

Georges Bizet

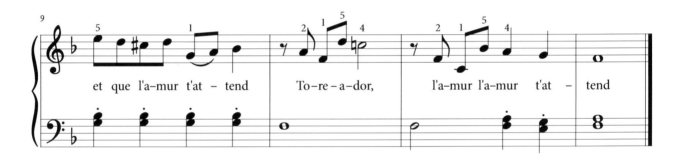

Bella Ciao

Italian Folk Song

Tarantella Napoletana

Traditional Italian

Minuet in D Minor

Johann Sebastian Bach

Eine kleine Nachtmusik
(Serenade No. 13 for strings in G major)

Wolfgang Amadeus Mozart

Allegro in F major
(K.1c)

Wolfgang Amadeus Mozart

Swan Lake

Pjotr Iljitsch Tschaikowski

Wedding March

Felix Mendelssohn

Scarborough Fair

Traditional English ballad

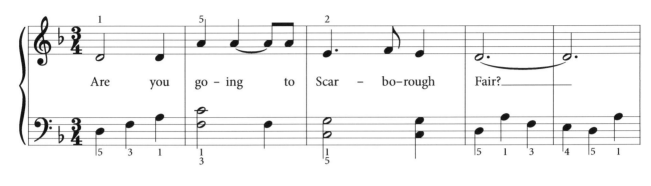

Are you go-ing to Scar – bo-rough Fair?

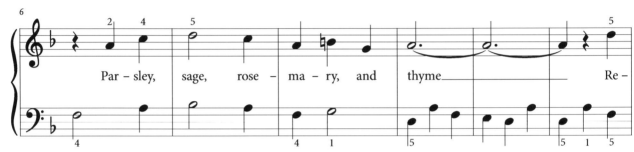

Par – sley, sage, rose – ma – ry, and thyme____ Re –

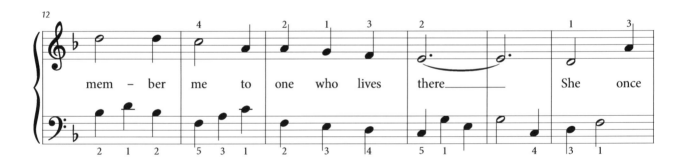

mem – ber me to one who lives there____ She once

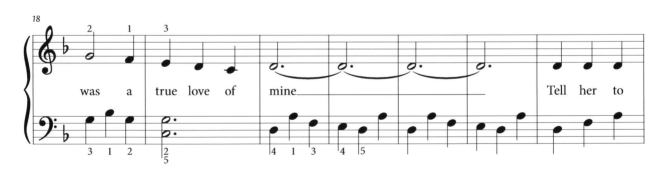

was a true love of mine____ Tell her to

The Blue Danube

Johann Strauss II

Für Elise

Ludwig van Beethoven

Caprice No. 24

Niccolò Paganini

The Entertainer

Scott Joplin

The Swan
(Le Cygne)

Camille Saint-Saëns

March
(The Nutcracker)

Pyotr Ilyich Tchaikovsky

Der Hölle Rache

(The Magic Flute)

Wolfgang Amadeus Mozart

Symphony No. 40
(Great G minor symphony)

Wolfgang Amadeus Mozart

72

Turkish March
(Turkish Rondo)

Wolfgang Amadeus Mozart

Hungarian Dance No. 5

Johannes Brahms

Adagio cantabile
(Sonata Pathétique)

Ludwig van Beethoven

Free Audio Files from the Book

This book also includes access to free audio recordings in mp3 format to help you learn and practice. The pieces were recorded by a professional pianist playing accurately and slowly each song on a piano so you know exactly what it should sound like.

HOW TO DOWNLOAD THE AUDIO FILES?

To download the audio files, go to the following link:

http://bit.ly/primopiano-audio-files

On the website, please enter your name and your email. Then, click "DOWNLOAD".

Go to the inbox of the email you have just entered. Find the email sent from "Sontig Press" with the subject "Please Confirm Your Subscription". If you cannot find the email, please also check your Spam or Promotions folders.

Once you have confirmed your email by clicking the button "CONFIRM YOUR EMAIL", you will receive a new email with the subject "Here are your audio files!". Clicking the link in the email (or the image) will give you an instant access to the audio recordings of the songs from the book!

You can download each file separately or all files at once (0. Audio files.zip).

Thank you for buying this book. If you are enjoying it, we'd like to ask you to leave a review for it on Amazon. It will take just a minute of your precious time.

Also, join our Facebook Group to get more free piano learning material (including free or discounted piano books, when published).

Do you have any questions or remarks about the book? If so, then send us an email at info@sontigpress.com and we'll be happy to help you.

Other Books by the Publisher

Timeless Piano Classics: 45 Beautiful Pieces of Classical Piano Music for Learners (+Free Audio)

Christina Levante

ASIN: 3982379512 *(type into Amazon search bar for quick lookup)*

In this book, you will find 45 splendid pieces of classical music for intermediate players.

The book features well-known world classical pieces as well as some beautiful less-known classics which often don't get enough recognition.

Little Pianist. Piano Songbook for Kids: Beginner Piano Sheet Music for Children with 55 Songs (+ Free Audio)

Aria Altmann

ASIN: 3982379504 *(type into Amazon search bar for quick lookup)*

In this book, you will find 55 very simple and easy songs for absolute beginners. All songs include fingerings and the easiest songs also include key letters.

The book features well-known children's songs and nursery rhymes, simplified classical pieces, as well as famous English evergreens and international folk songs.

Primo Piano. Easy Piano Music for Adults. 55 Timeless Piano Songs for Adult Beginners with Downloadable Audio by Aria Altmann

2. edition 2021
ISBN: 978-3-9822692-1-4
Sontig Press

Printed in Great Britain
by Amazon

87089549R00052